Thank you for your service —
Loving Jes.

SEE

WITH CHRIST

Like a child, we come Luke 18:16

The Lord is my Shepherd, I shall not want…
Psalm 23:1 (KJV)

In Christ, 🐑 *Estella*
& Bob who wrote TRUSTING HIM.

Estella Boomsma
Copyright © 2021

For children of all ages, short, fictionalized stories
from true family events.
Includes true spiritual experiences and Biblical promises
that comforted & empowered them in their journey
through the changing seasons of life.

DEDICATED TO:
My Beloved Husband.
My Lord and Savior Jesus Christ,
and all His God-kids everywhere.

Fictionalized Memoirs & Spiritual Lessons

PERMISSIONS: All Bible verses are quoted and noted as follows, and given gratis permission, since less than 25% of this publication, and less than 500 scriptures, are taken from the following Bible versions:

KJV – King James Version, Cambridge: *Scripture quotations from The Authorized (King James) Version. Rights in the Authorized Version in the United Kingdom are vested in the Crown, Reproduced by permission of the Crown's patentee, Cambridge University Press.*

NIV – New International Version, Biblica. *Scripture quotations taken from The Holy Bible, New International Version® NIV® Copyright © 1973 1978 1984 2011 by Biblica, Inc. TM Used by permission. All rights reserved worldwide.*

TLB – The Living Bible, Tyndale House. *Scripture quotations marked (TLB) are taken from The Living Bible copyright © 1971. Used by permission of Tyndale House Publishers, Carol Stream, Illinois 60188. All rights reserved.*

JETLAUNCH

PREFACE

Over a year since the COVID-19 pandemic began, this book was initially written for my God-kids so that they would know some of my family background and how several generations trusted God during incredibly stressful difficult times. There is nothing new under the sun.

Each life has difficult seasons, each life has opportunity to TURN TO GOD, AND NOT AWAY FROM HIM, with each new challenge.

As Corrie ten Boom told after her concentration camp experience in World War II, she said that even in the darkest pit, God will come to you.

Thus, another purpose for this book emerged, and that is to encourage the readers toward more "knee-action" than "re-action," no matter what time or season you are in now.

Perhaps pray before reading herein. Bow in prayer within your inner self and ask God to light up those words of truth that will set you free in this moment. His loving words assure us of His Presence, and we become set free from panic and trauma the more we meditate on them.

As in the pandemic, even though death is all around you, choose life. Focus on Christ who is spirit and life. Love Him, give your heart to Him. Jesus Christ is our Savior who continues to save. Christ took eternal justice for us all on the cross, now we are free to love and give our lives for others, with the help of His Spirit. Just surrender and trust.

Choose life in your loving, in your worship, in the depths within your heart. Choose life. Speak life. Read it. Love it. Let the Bible give your mind images of what true life and love look like.

Embrace each small evidence of life, and let it make you smile. Smile at others, and you send a little life to them. Apologize if you offend. Say "God Bless you" often to those around you.

Go into the Holy place within you, and know who you are as a spirit being, and whose you are and that you belong to Christ. He is always with you, and you are never alone.

No time to argue about God. No time to wonder if He exists. Just take the thought, saying to yourself and others, "Trust in God."

God is within you. Get it straight about who you are. You are made in the image of God, a little trinity of Mind, Body, and Spirit. Know who He is, as the Father, Son, and Holy Spirit. Let Him give you back your wholeness as you focus on Christ and meditate on His Love.

Let yourself esteem the holy temple that you are. Forgive yourself with Jesus words from the Cross, "Father forgive them & me for we know not what we do." Then Bless and release others with the same prayer.

Set them free to be, to be recreated by Him who was resurrected from the dead, and who will resurrect us daily, too.

As we continue TRUSTING HIM, Christ will help us REST in His Love.

TABLE OF CONTENTS

With Scriptures

2 Corinthians 4:18 KJV "*While we look not at the things which are seen, but at the things that are not seen: for the things which are seen are temporal; but the things which are not seen are eternal.*"

John 14:18 NIV "*I will not leave you as orphans, I will come to you.*" (*Jesus*)

Romans 8:28-29KJV "*And we know that all things work together for good to them that love God, to them who are the called according to His purpose. ... to be conformed to the image of His Son.*"

Matthew 5:8 *"Blessed are the pure in heart: for they shall see God."*

1 Corinthians 15:44 & 49 KJV *"There is a natural body, and there is a spiritual body. ... And as we have borne the image of the earthy, we shall also bear the image of the heavenly."*

1 Thessalonians 5:23 KJV *"...I pray God that your whole SPIRIT and SOUL (psyche) and BODY be preserved blameless unto the coming of our Lord Jesus* Christ."

Psalm 34:5 KJV *"They looked unto Him, and were lightened: and their faces were not ashamed."*

John 11:25-26 NIV *"Jesus said to her, I am the resurrection and the life. He who believes in Me will live, even though he dies; and whoever lives and believes in Me will never die. Do you believe this?"*

Psalm 46:10 NIV *"Be still, and know that I am God; I will be exalted among the nations, I will be exalted in the earth."*

Psalm 34: 7 KJV *"The angel of the Lord encampeth round about them that fear Him, and delivereth them."*

Jeremiah 29:11 TLB *"For I know the plans I have for you, says the Lord. They are plans for good and not for evil, to give you a future and a hope."*

Isaiah 41:10-13KJV *"Fear thou not; for I am with thee: be not dismayed; for I am thy God: I will strengthen thee; yea, I will help thee; yea, I will uphold thee with the right hand of my righteousness. Behold, all they that were incensed against thee*

shall be ashamed and confounded; they shall be as nothing;…
For I the Lord thy God will hold thy right hand, saying unto
thee, Fear not, I will help thee."

Psalm 91:11 KJV *"For He shall give His angels charge over*
thee to keep thee in all thy ways."

John 14:27 NIV *"Peace I leave with you; my peace I give you.*
I do not give to you as the world gives. Do not let your hearts
be troubled and do not be afraid."

1 John 4:4 KJV *"Ye are of God, little children, and have*
overcome them: because greater is He that is in you, than he
that is in the world."

"And we have known and believed the love that God hath to us.
God is love; and he that dwelleth in love dwelleth in God, and
God in him. … as He is, so are we in this world. There is no fear
in love; but perfect love casteth out fear…" (1 John 4:16-18 KJV)

2 Corinthians 12:9 KJV *"My Grace is sufficient for thee: for*
my strength is made perfect in weakness."

Isaiah 41:13 KJV *"Fear not, I will help thee."*

Psalm 91:4 KJV *"Under His Wings thou shalt trust…"*

Jeremiah 29:11 NIV *" "For I know the plans I have for you*
declares the Lord, plans to prosper you and not to harm you,
plans to give you a hope and a future."

"For God hath not given us the spirit of fear; but of power, and of love, and of a sound mind." (2 Timothy 1:7 KJV)

Isaiah 46:4 NIV *"Even to your old age and gray hairs I am He, I am He who will sustain you. I have made you and I will carry you; I will sustain you and I will rescue you."*

Isaiah 50:4 KJV *"The Lord God hath given me the tongue of the learned, that I should know how to speak a word in season to him that is weary: He wakeneth morning by morning, He wakeneth mine ear to hear as the learned."*

John 15:5 NIV *"I am the vine, you are the branches. If a man remains in me and I in him, he will bear much fruit; apart from me you can do nothing."*

Psalm 31:15 KJV *"My times are in thy hand…"*

John 6:29 KJV "Jesus answered and said unto them, This is the work of God, that ye believe on him whom He hath sent."

Psalm 1:3 KJV *"And he shall be like a tree planted by the rivers of water, that bringeth forth his fruit in His season; his leaf also shall not wither; and whatsoever he doeth shall prosper."*

Eccl.3:1 KJV *"To everything there is a season and a time for every purpose under the heaven."*

Psalm 37:3 & 7 KJV *"Trust in the Lord, and do good … Rest in the Lord, and wait patiently for Him: fret not thyself …"*

Haggai 2:9 KJV *"The glory of this latter house shall be greater than of the former, saith the Lord of hosts: and in this place will I give peace, saith the Lord of hosts."*

Philippians 1:6 KJV *"Being confident of this very thing, that He which hath begun a good work in you will perform it until the day of Jesus Christ."*

Psalm 23 KJV

1 "The Lord is my Shepherd; I shall not want.

2 He maketh me to lie down in green pastures: he leadeth me beside the still waters.

3 He restoreth my soul: he leadeth me in the paths of righteousness for his name's sake.

4 Yea, though I walk through the valley of the shadow of death, I will fear no evil: for thou art with me; thy rod and thy staff they comfort me.

5 Thou preparest a table before me in the presence of mine enemies: thou anointest my head with oil: my cup runneth over.

6 Surely goodness and mercy shall follow me all the days of my life: and I will dwell in the house of the Lord for ever."

Isaiah 53:4-6 NIV "Surely he took up our infirmities and carried our sorrows ... the punishment that brought us peace was upon him, and by His wounds we are healed.

We all, like sheep, have gone astray, each 🐑 of us has turned to his own way; and the Lord has laid on Him the iniquity of us all."

John 14:18 & 21 NIV "I will not leave you as orphans; I will come to you ... He who loves Me will be loved by my Father, and I too will love him and show myself to him."

Isaiah 54:1-3 NIV "Sing, O barren woman (OR BARREN LIFE), you who never bore a child, burst into song ... because more are the children of the desolate ... Enlarge the place of your tent ... do not hold back; lengthen your cords, strengthen your stakes. ... For you will spread out to the right and to the left."

1 John 4:1-2 NIV "Dear friends, do not believe every spirit, but test the spirits to see whether they are from God ... Every spirit that acknowledges that Jesus Christ has come in the flesh is from God."

1 John 1:5 NIV "... GOD IS LIGHT; in Him there is no darkness at all."

Psalm 104:2 KJV "Who coverest thyself with LIGHT as with a garment."

John 8:12 NIV "When Jesus spoke again to the people, he said, 'I AM THE LIGHT OF THE WORLD. WHOEVER FOLLOWS ME WILL NEVER WALK IN DARKNESS BUT WILL HAVE THE LIGHT OF LIFE.'"

1

A GIRL NAMED PEARL

2 Corinthians 4:18 KJV "*While we look not at the things which are seen, but at the things that are not seen: for the things which are seen are temporal; but the things which are not seen are eternal.*"

John 14:18 NIV "*I will not leave you as orphans, I will come to you.*" (*Jesus*)

Once upon a time in the 1800's, a beautiful young girl named Pearl was born to a family who had recently immigrated to Canada to escape civil unrest in the land of their birth. They even changed their name in order to protect from persecution. Name changes were common in those days. Names also have been changed in this book, to protect privacy.

Pearl enjoyed the open spaces in Prince Edward County, along Lake Ontario, Canada. Pearl's family belonged to the local parish church where Pearl and her two younger sisters loved to worship and play with the other children in this beautiful town by the lake. Life was good.

Then things changed suddenly. To her dismay, her parents got sick in an epidemic and died suddenly. These three little girls were very sad. Life hurt.

In their fear and grief they clung to each other, and to Jesus Christ as they had been taught at church. Now they had to make Him real in their hearts.

They learned to SEE BEYOND, TURNING TO GOD AND NOT AWAY FROM HIM, TRUSTING CHRIST TO REDEEM, in spite of their situation—"Accepting" what is, and "Expecting" more from God.

Thankfully, they were connected to their extended family in the United States, who heard of their need and provided homes. Unfortunately, their new homes were separate from one another. One sister went to live with an Aunt, another to a distant cousin in Upstate New York. Pearl went to live with her grandparents.

Pearl knew that her earthly father was now "with God", thus as she drew near to God in her thoughts, she also was "with God", and felt closer to her family who were "with God" too. Pearl embraced her Bible, and in so doing, she embraced Jesus as Savior and constant friend. She could not bring back her parents nor sisters, but she could seek Jesus and ask that His Spirit "Redeem" her circumstances.

Pearl grew up in her grandparent's home and eventually met a handsome young man whose parents were evangelists. Their hearts meshed since they both loved Jesus, and they loved one another, too. Indeed, "Christ Redeemed." The sadness in her life was comforted by a big new family through her husband. Pearl experienced a happy new season of lots of love.

Children came along to Pearl and her husband. They had one daughter and two sons. As the children grew into teenagers, Pearl started feeling pain in her bones, which the cold winters up north aggravated. Thus, her family decided to move south to a warmer climate. It was during the Great Depression, nevertheless for health reasons, they took courage and moved to warmer weather on the southwest coast of California. At first they sold popcorn on street corners to pay for dinner. But, doors opened, and her husband found a good job as a machinist. God provided. Life was good. Their life had another season of happiness.

Then, a few years later, another season of sadness, when Pearl's teenage daughter went swimming in the ocean with friends and got pneumonia. There were no antibiotics in those days, so their dear daughter lost her fight with that infection and died at age 18. Grief, loss, hurt, felt like a knot in the stomach.

Sometimes grief feels like fear. The family needed time to acknowledge this deep loss, thus for a while, it was a season of silence. "Surrender & Trust." Pearl rested in God. Christ's Spirit was her continual comfort in both life and death.

Then God provided another season of happiness. It was a welcome surprise when Pearl's beloved son, Edward, married Lillian from Lily. Pearl loved her new daughter-in-law as if she were her own. Pearl and Lillian became close friends and prayer partners. God provided loving spiritual support to Pearl through

Lillian, even when Pearl got sick with bone cancer. Pearl died at age 55, with Lillian by her side, and Jesus welcoming her spirit into His new home for her in  Heaven. Home at last. No more sad seasons.

Pearl learned to SEE BEYOND, at every turn in life, trusting CHRIST TO REDEEM everything. Her heart always had a home in Jesus, no matter where they lived, no matter what she experienced.

PERSONAL APPLICATION:

Where do you feel at home today? Will you ask Christ to be your Savior for all eternity so that your spirit will go safely with Him to Heaven?

Have you noticed Jesus providing a prayer partner for you in this season of life? Perhaps Jesus is your only prayer partner right now. Yes, He is enough. And, He will help you "surrender & trust," so that you can feel His comfort. Pray and wait. Our Good Shepherd will help you SEE BEYOND.

2

LOVING LILY

Romans 8:28-29KJV *"And we know that all things work together for good to them that love God, to them who are the called according to His purpose. ... to be conformed to the image of His Son."*

Matthew 5:8 "Blessed are the pure in heart: for they shall see God."

It was after the turn of the century, early 1900's. Lily was a small farm town being built by pioneering families in their day. One of the couples thought about naming their first daughter born in that town after the town's name Lily. But they changed their minds and named her Lillian, so that she had her own individuality.

Much work and effort went into building this new town of Lily, and Lillian's father helped establish a bank. They lived in an apartment behind the bank, where little Lillian was born. Years later, they moved to another home on a small farm where this growing family with seven children lived happily for almost 20 years.

On their farm, they raised sheep. One of Lillian's favorite stories was about watching the gamboling lambs in the spring.

As the winter gave way to warmer weather, the baby lambs would stretch their legs and hop gleefully, often forming a circle on the hill, and dance around as if someone had taught them. It reminded Lillian that our Heavenly Father has a "dance" for us at the end of every winter in our life.

As Psalm 23 says, When the Lord is our Shepherd ... Goodness and mercy will follow. Wait for it. Spring always comes "after" winters.

After Lil graduated from Lily High School, the Great Depression was just beginning. Then the stock market crashed. People "ran on the bank" out of fear and withdrew all their money. Thus, the bank had to close. Lil's dad was now out of work. This family of seven children had to be relocated. Taking time to grieve their losses and TURN TO GOD again, and NOT AWAY FROM GOD, the family decided to send their older daughter, Lillian, to California to look for work. They were forced to SEE BEYOND their circumstances, and trust God's promise to work all things together for good to those who Love Him.

Thus, Lil took courage, as she and one other sister rode with trusted friends to California, hoping to find work and a new place to live. Her dad had trained her in banking, therefore she quickly found a job as a clerk in a bank in Southern California. At least she had some income to help other family members as they migrated, looking for new jobs, looking for new places to settle.

Lillian saw God's hand in opening doors for her. Yes, some doors shut. BUT GOD opens other doors. In fact, it was at her church where Lillian met handsome Edward (Pearl's son, who migrated from Upstate New York). They had something in common. Both Ed and Lil's families were forced by circumstances to move to California during the Great Depression. They felt God had a hand in this because they fell in love and married.

Edward and Lillian bought some land, raised chickens, first stayed in tents, then built a small home. Several of Lil's family moved from the Midwest and stayed with them for short periods of time before they established their own homes and jobs. Ed's younger brother eventually became the pastor in the town church.

They had a great season of happiness. They called this their "honeymoon" years.

Then World War II broke out. Lillian's husband, Edward, went to war in the South Pacific as a Pharmacist Mate for the Navy. Now it was again a challenge to TURN TO GOD, and NOT AWAY. The Spirit of Life in Christ would become "real" to her as she would "surrender & trust." Again she learned to SEE BEYOND, trusting that God would work all things together for good. It was a season of serious faith, waiting on God.

World War II came to an end. After three years in the South Pacific, Lillian's beloved husband Edward came home from serving with the Navy. He found a job working at the Post Office as a Letter Carrier in their small town. They also continued raising chickens and selling eggs. They were deeply grateful for life and for God's love in their hearts. Thus, Ed and Lil wanted to start a family.

Another season of happiness began.

PERSONAL APPLICATION:

When life disappoints you, have you practiced TURNING TO GOD and NOT AWAY FROM HIM? Have you asked Him to help you SEE BEYOND your

current circumstances, trusting His Love to work all things together for your good?

Even when you feel fear, are you aware that things happen so that the "image of Christ" becomes formed in you, as you learn to "surrender & trust".

As Christ's humility and love begin to take hold and grow within you, then you become ready for another "happy season" where you can encourage others with what you learned, without being prideful.

"The Lord is our Shepherd, we shall not want… "(Psalm 23:1 KJV)

3

LITTLE STAR

1 Corinthians 15:44 & 49 KJV "*There is a natural body, and there is a spiritual body. ... And as we have borne the image of the earthy, we shall also bear the image of the heavenly.*"

1 Thessalonians 5:23 KJV "*...I pray God that your whole SPIRIT and SOUL (psyche) and BODY be preserved blameless unto the coming of our Lord Jesus* Christ."

Psalm 34:5 KJV "*They looked unto Him, and were lightened: and their faces were not ashamed.*"

A baby girl was born to Lillian and Edward the year after World War II came to an end. They named her Star.

Baby's often give new life to families in grief. Thus, this family rejoiced and were renewed and encouraged. Lil had several miscarriages before the War, but this time, after the War, little Star grew full term and was born healthy. God's timing was perfect. Another happy season. Time to do a happy dance.

Lil and Ed would dance around their living room to Lawrence Welk's band on TV. Like the gamboling lambs on the farm after the winter seasons, Ed & Lil danced too after the winters of the Great Depression and World War II.

Life was good.

The new schools in their neighborhood made it easy for little Star to walk to school from kindergarten through high school. These were indeed "happy days."

Edward & Lillian also loved foreign missions. In Mexico on one of their visits, Lillian's spirit had an open vision of Christ while she was walking through a garden visiting Misión San Ignacio, Magdalena, Sonora, Mexico. She saw Jesus standing between Heaven and Earth, and all coming down to earth through Him. His desire is to save us all. But Lillian said she thought we needed to "look TO Him", in other words open our heart and "receive Him", like a friend, Savior, in order for spirit-connection to happen, as in any relationship.

"Relationship" is everything. Thus, Lil taught her daughter Star to say, "Jesus I repent of my sins and receive you as my Lord and Savior. Thank you Lord for being my friend."

Star fell in love with Jesus too and trusted Him within her spirit as eternal Savior and friend. What Star also became aware of was that we all have a visible physical body, but we also have an invisible spiritual-self. Some call it our "heart." Our spirit-self lives forever, even past our physical body, thus it's important to "choose" where we want our spirit to spend eternity. Do we want our spirit-self to live with Christ in Heaven, or do we want to stay in chaos forever. Star chooses Christ and Heaven.

At a Billy Graham Crusade, Star and her high school sweetheart, Robert, went forward to "formally" surrender to Christ and receive His Spirit, asking for His wisdom and strength to do His will for their lives.

A couple years after high school, Star and Robert married. They went to State colleges and then worked hard at good jobs. Favor followed them. They were experiencing Psalm 23 where in the beginning we embrace, "The Lord is my Shepherd", then at the end of Psalm 23, it says "Surely goodness and mercy shall follow me."

They built a house near the snow-peaked mountains. These were the same mountains Star loved to look at in childhood, at a distance, from her mom's

kitchen window. It seemed like all her dreams had come true at a young age.

Life was good.

Then Star experienced an auto-immune disorder that caused her chronic fatigue. So, after 13 years working at a wonderful job as an Executive Secretary in a large Corporation, she took an extended medical leave, then eventually left the corporate world. During her medical leave, she had a God-dream:

Star's vision: In a dream one night God showed Star's spirit a glimpse of Heaven on the other side of a river. There was a rainbow that had more colors in it than what we see on earth, and it was so beautiful she wanted to cross the river. In the dream, Star was sitting with Jesus on the grass on this earthly side of the river, and He said to her, "even though you love the beauty that you SEE BEYOND, you must stay on this side of the river and help people get to know me more."

Thus, Star felt she had personal instruction from the Lord to share about His Love, encouraging people to seek His Presence, a personal relationship with Christ. Her health recovered enough to work part-time at missions agencies, which began a wonderful new happy chapter in her life.

PERSONAL APPLICATION:

Where is Jesus inviting you to sit with Him and enjoy the beauty of His Presence in the present?

Jesus also helps us form our true identity. Has Christ imparted to you a sense that you are more than what you see, that you are also a spirit-being inside needing to be fed with His Love?

Have you noticed that when you look into the mirror, you see a little trinity of mind, body, and spirit? Three expressions of one person, you. The Bible says we were created in the image of God, who also is three expressions, yet ONE PERSON:

Father, Son, and Holy Spirit. He is the ALMIGHTY TRINITY.

John 11:25-26 NIV *"Jesus said to her, I am the resurrection and the life. He who believes in Me will live, even though he dies; and whoever lives and believes in Me will never die. Do you believe this?"* YES, LORD, WE BELIEVE.

4

MR. ROBERT LAUNCHING MISSIONS

Psalm 46:10 NIV *"Be still, and know that I am God; I will be exalted among the nations, I will be exalted in the earth."*

Psalm 34: 7 KJV *"The angel of the Lord encampeth round about them that fear Him, and delivereth them."*

Jeremiah 29:11 TLB *"For I know the plans I have for you, says the Lord. They are plans for good and not for evil, to give you a future and a hope."*

Mr. Robert got his college degree in Sociology, which the Lord used in networking, bringing people and projects together in both business and missions. First the Lord gave him business experience, using his networking skills to fund businesses. That gave him both grief and grit, but also staying power to do what God needed him to do later in missions as he traveled the world and represented missions work to Christian Foundations and business executives.

On one of his mission trips to Mongolia, Robert had an open spiritual vision. He saw a little girl in front of him in a very noisy crowded line pushing to  get on an airplane. The little girl looked orphaned, desperately sad and afraid, who seemed to be saying to him even though they didn't speak each other's language, "I'm so lonely and afraid." In compassion he reached out to her, but then she was gone. It was only a vision. Or, perhaps it was an angel messenger.

Nevertheless, the image put a lasting impression in Robert's heart. He felt it was a supernatural message from the Lord to continue his job of spreading the good news to the world. People need to know that Christ is Risen, His Spirit is always present, available for us to draw near with our hearts and receive comfort and provision. As it says in Psalm 46:10 "Be still and know that I am God."

The vision in Mongolia gave Robert motivation to continue his work, pressing on during the hard times in missions. As he studied other missionaries of old, none of them had a perfect life. Satan, who the Bible calls the "adversary," opposes all good, and tries to discourage God's messengers from their work of spreading the good news of God's Love through Christ.

Robert's only brother, Roger, was killed in the Viet Nam War. But, before he died, Roger wrote how he was feeding orphans in Viet Nam who were relying on Marines to feed them after their families had died. Roger asked for more packages to be sent to him with food items for the orphans. But, a few weeks later he was killed. Twenty years later, a young Vietnamese man came to Robert's front porch seeking a job as a gardener. It turned out he was an orphan in Viet Nam during that time Roger was there, and he was fed by Marines too. It seemed coincidental. Roger fed "physical food" to Viet Nam orphans, so Robert felt compelled to feed this young man "spiritual food" to give him "assurance" of eternal life through trusting Christ as Savior. Robert hired him as his gardener.

Robert was also asked to mentor the gardener's oldest son. Thus, Robert became "Uncle Bob", which was fulfilling for them both. Christ redeems losses. It does not mean we don't miss the old, it just means we embrace the new. We believe that is one of the ways "Christ Redeems."

Robert continued using God's giftings in his life to bring people and projects together for God's Kingdom. Even in retirement, people would call him for counsel. He would counsel from his fund-raising experience, and he would also do pastoral counseling from his heart of compassion. People would often call him for prayer for healing. He would be asked to stand up at weddings, do eulogies, and share his life experiences in small groups.

Like Joseph's story in the Bible, even in Robert's innocent serving, motivated by compassion, some insecure people would get jealous and resistant. And, like Joseph, Robert continued "Trusting God" at every turn.

Robert would pray for those who persecuted him, praying Jesus prayer from the Cross, "Father forgive them, and us, for we know not what we do." Thus, he was able to "bless and release" difficult people and entrust them to God who perfects that which concerns us all as we look TO Him. Jesus wants to save us all.

Robert was a Prince in the eyes of his wife, as she saw his sacrifices and service. Even in old age, he was her loving and comforting companion. God's blessings were upon him always, as it promises in following scripture:

"Fear thou not; for I am with thee: be not dismayed; for I am thy God: I will strengthen thee; yea, I will help thee; yea, I will uphold thee with the right hand of my righteousness. Behold, all they that were incensed against thee shall be ashamed and confounded; they shall be as nothing;... For I the Lord thy God will hold thy right hand, saying unto thee, Fear not, I will help thee." (Isaiah 41:10,11,13 KJV).

PERSONAL APPLICATION:

Is it a challenge for you to be still and look to God, getting out of His way, letting go and letting God do

that which you cannot do?

Are you willing to pour out your feelings to God? Then, let His "compassion" fill your empty places so that you can SEE BEYOND the surface of difficult people: Often it's just fear within a hurting heart, needing to be healed by Christ's love. Are you willing to ask God to heal their heart, and your heart? Willing to forgive, pray for, bless and release them to God – to step out of the way, so that God can make them whole, and you whole?

5

GUARDIAN ANGELA

Psalm 91:11 KJV *"For He shall give His angels charge over thee to keep thee in all thy ways."*

John 14:27 NIV *"Peace I leave with you; my peace I give you. I do not give to you as the world gives. Do not let your hearts be troubled and do not be afraid."*

 Robert and Star had no children. But when, through missions they met a young Spanish girl who looked like an Angel, their hearts were quickened with joy.

Angela often took it upon herself to guard her sisters from assault in their instable neighborhood. She was like a "Guardian Angel," as if "called" to stand up to evil and "just say no" to evil assaults. Her father had disappeared in Mexico. Her mother had gone looking for him, and thus she disappeared too.

At a young age, Angela was told by her grandmother to look to God as her true Father, because her Heavenly Father could always be with her. Thus, Angela began to SEE BEYOND her difficult circumstances, leaning on Christ's Spirit as her friend and guide.

A pastor decided to help and looked for families to take one of the girls since their mother and father had disappeared. Thus, through personal connections, through their network of friends, this pastor found Mr. Robert & Star who offered to invite Angela to live with them in their home. Therefore, this childless couple became "Legal Guardians." Because it was a year of amnesty, they were quickly able to get Angela documented, and later she became a U.S. Citizen and a gifted professional woman.

Angela lived with these Guardians for a wonderful year of giving and receiving love for one another. This was a healing time for Angela. Also, a healing time for her new Guardians. The three of them attended a new church that was full of life. One of their activities was to feed the public in the downtown mission. It was training for Heaven where we give out continually as God gives to us.

Angela was a "natural" who spoke Spanish to those who needed it when she served food with the church group. She served them lovingly and generously, "like a Guardian Angel."

Angela also went to summer camp with the young people of this church, and she received the Joy of Baptism by the Holy Spirit. As she opened up her heart more to Him, a variety of "heart-talk" became more joyful and overflowing, and she felt a new connectivity with His Spirit.

This was a new dimension of spiritual growth for Angela, even though she already had been taught at a young age, when living with her grandmother, to rely on God. She always had strength within her to stand up for what's right and just. But Joy-Talk, Heart-Talk, surpassing head knowledge, just relaxing into His Spirit within her was a new thing. It was SEEING BEYOND.

After a year had passed, Angela's mother came back from Mexico and Angela wanted to return to her since her mom wanted to try again to be a stable family.

Angela shared one of her favorite scriptures to lean on at that time: 1 John 4:4 KJV "*Ye are of God, little children, and have overcome them: because greater is He that is in you, than he that is in the world.*" She envisioned God's strength would be with her and in her.

Angela's new Guardians were very sad to see her go, but they stayed in touch as friends for the rest of their lives. One of the favorite things Angela mentioned to her Guardians before she left was to thank them for their time of devotions at the end of each day: Sitting together they would read the Bible, Proverbs, Psalms, and other devotionals. Then they would talk about their day, and how to apply the wisdom of God's Words.

They all learned that when difficult circumstances come, we can look to God and lean on His promises. Sometimes, we just have to "accept what is", then "trust Christ to redeem" at every turn in life: Be still and know that He is God, and that He has a plan better than ours.

PERSONAL APPLICATION:

 Do you feel guarded by love by someone in your life? Have you ever felt supernatural moments of peace, as if God or one of His Guardian Angels were near?

"And we have known and believed the love that God hath to us. God is love; and he that dwelleth in love dwelleth in God, and God in him. ... as He is, so are we in this world. There is no fear in love; but perfect love casteth out fear..." (1 John 4:16-18 KJV)

6

PEACEFUL PRINCESS

2 Corinthians 12:9 KJV *"My Grace is sufficient for thee: for my strength is made perfect in weakness."*

Isaiah 41:13 KJV *"Fear not, I will help thee."*

 It was a happy surprise when a young student in Pastoral Care Counseling came to stay with Robert and Star to be "extra family." She had such peace, she looked like a "Princess", so that's what they called her. No one replaces previous loved ones, but God can "add to" the loves we have. As Christ says, He always goes to prepare a place for us, both in His heart and home (John 14:2). Therefore, we also have a special place in our heart for each new person that comes into our lives.

Prior to a board meeting, Robert and Star were asked if they would pick up a young student who had a scholarship and bring her to the business dinner. YES, they said, they were delighted to pick her up and give her a ride to the board dinner.

Her sweet eyes reflected a sincere heart, and they bonded immediately. This was a vision that didn't go away. It was a gift from God for the next two decades.

During this time, Robert and Star became Grandparents. Two sons were born to Princess as her husband commuted back and forth from his job overseas. Grandpa and Grandma felt so happy and privileged to have been with Princess the actual "day" each son was born. It was a thrill in their life to see Princess go graciously into the hospital to deliver her babies, and a privilege to bless the boys the first day of their life upon this earth. These babies were gifts from Heaven. Also Princess's real mom came for the birth of both the boys and would talk delightedly with Grandma Star, neither understanding each other's physical language, but both understanding the language of their hearts, a celebration within one another's spirit. Their "heart-talk" was simply JOY overflowing.

There is more than one dimension in which to communicate.

Life was good. Christmas Day was always special at Grandpa and Grandma's house in their small town. The local firetrucks would drive by passing out peanuts and candy to all the children who came up to the fire truck. Then, the boys would come back inside the house for prayer before eating the Christmas mid-day dinner.

After the Christmas meal would be "the reading". They would be reminded of the Christmas Story of Christ being born into this world supernaturally through Mary's surrender to the Holy Spirit. This reminds each of us that when we surrender to the Spirit of Life in Christ Jesus, He will also show up in and through our lives too.

They would also read short Christian stories, discussing spiritual applications of trusting Christ to Redeem, and giving thanks to God for His Gift of Jesus Christ, our Savior, whose birthday we celebrate at Christmas. After the readings, they'd open gifts. Then, Grandpa Robert would play Carems game with the boys. Princess and Grandma Star would clean up the kitchen and talk. Then instead of naps, they would watch a good Christian movie to feed their souls.

Life was good.

The oldest son reminds Grandma Star of the spiritual name "Braveheart" because he courageously led the way into activities, especially music as he played the piano in public, and coached his younger brother along life's ways. "Caringheart" is a good spiritual name for the youngest son who puts to good use writ-

ten words, especially nice was his "Thankful List" he gave to Grandpa one Father's Day, listing ten things he was so thankful for. Grandpa Robert loved it.

Grandpa and Grandma were so proud of both these strong grandsons, strong in spirit, strong in "Trusting Christ to Redeem." Honored to see both baptized by immersion, Grandpa gave them special hats afterwards, with the words: "Christ Followers International". A reminder Who they eternally "belong" to, and Who "covers" them always:

Clothed with Christ. "Under His Wings thou shalt trust" (Psalm 91:4 KJV).

Several years later, during the serious COVID-19 pandemic of 2020, many pressures inserted themselves into many lives. Princess also experienced poor health and pressures, which brought her to her knees before the Lord. She felt like her own strength was gone. Thankfully, she had training in pastoral counseling at the University, thus she had help from her peers, and professional expertise to lean on as well as the Lord. Thanking God He provided "extra" people to provide courage, guidance, and practical help.

During the pandemic, Grandpa and Grandma would send encouragement by texts, adding God's promises from scripture when it seemed appropriate. Also sent mail-order cookies and snacks to cheer them while they were confined in their home. Cookies and milk refresh the body, and God's loving promises of His Presence refresh the soul.

Isaiah 41:13 KJV "For I the Lord thy God will hold thy right hand, saying unto thee, Fear not, I will help thee."

Princess would say often, God's Grace and Strength are sufficient for me, God's strength is made perfect in my weakness. In spite of experiencing hard times, I am willing to trust that God is good.

Yes, we can trust that our good Shepherd will "restore" us in His time, and guide us in beneficial paths. He will be with us in the valleys, and prepare a table before us with goodness and love. (Psalm 23:3-6).

Princess gave Grandpa and Grandma a wonderful thank-you gift with the Bible verse from the Lord written on it: Jeremiah 29:11 NIV

"For I know the plans I have for you ... plans to prosper you and not to harm you, plans to give you a hope and a future." This is a good promise for all of us to lean on.

Princess and her sons focused on school during the pandemic, taking on-line classes. Both she and they now have several graduations to celebrate.

PERSONAL APPLICATION:

Do you believe God is good? When life seems traumatic are you willing to ask God to guide you to His professional mentors in every area of your life? What scriptures from the Bible are speaking strength into you during this season? Have you written those words of life where you can see them often, or in a journal?

"For God hath not given us the spirit of fear; but of power, and of love, and of a sound mind." (2 Timothy 1:7 KJV)

7

SEEING BEYOND
RETIREMENT

Isaiah 46:4 NIV *"Even to your old age and gray hairs I am He, I am He who will sustain you. I have made you and I will carry you; I will sustain you and I will rescue you."*

Isaiah 50:4 KJV *"The Lord God hath given me the tongue of the learned, that I should know how to speak a word in season to him that is weary: He wakeneth morning by morning, He wakeneth mine ear to hear as the learned."*

John 15:5 NIV *"I am the vine, you are the branches. If a man remains in me and I in him, he will bear much fruit; apart from me you can do nothing."*

As in Jesus first miracle, turning WATER INTO WINE, so is maturing in Christ. Like fine wine, retirement can be a time of deep satisfaction, drinking in the fruits of the Spirit from Christ.

How does "maturing in Christ" happen? Think about how wine is made and what happens to grapes before they are quarantined, before fermentation. Grapes are first crushed, then put away for a season of silence until fermentation develops flavor in the wine.

Have you ever been crushed? Broken, humbled, stepped on?

Have you ever been quarantined, imprisoned, limited? How has that changed you?

There's an old saying, we can either get "bitter or better" when life molds us into something unrecognizable. We become "better" when we can surrender and say, Lord, "*My times are in Thy hand...*" (Psalm 31:15 KJV). In other words, once again, we can choose to TURN TO GOD, AND NOT AWAY.

In the year of 2020, during the pandemic, our world shifted from regular social contact to social distancing. But God provided, just in time, the tool of technology to help people stay connected by WORDS.

Thus, for retirees, a new Ministry of Encouragement by Email and Zoom became a joyful privilege, sharing wine of maturity in Christ. So, the year of 2020, was also a year of WORDS. We can choose to be healers by reversing the trend of negative words by intentionally inserting positive words of faith and love which feed our spirits.

"I believe statements" are a wonderful way to speak life into others when they are floundering. "Belief statements" can't be argued with, since a person's belief stands alone for them to own. Thus, we can say, "I believe God will help you with that." "I believe you are better than that." "I believe you'll experience more of God each day." "I believe Christ will come to you if you ask Him." "I believe you'll be OK."

God's Spirit motivated God Lovers throughout the ages to "write" His words of assurance and love in the Bible. We, too, can write words of love and assurance in Christ. God is using all these things, to prepare us all, for Heaven and for SEEING BEYOND.

"*To everything there is a season and a time for every purpose under the heaven.*" (Eccl.3:1KJV). This season of time on this earth is only "practice", the "trial" period, preparing us for the new heavens and new earth. And, as the saying goes, "when we rest, we pass the test." We learn to REST in the knowledge of His Love, within our inner self.

Resurrection power doesn't require effort, it requires REST, so that we get out of God's way, let Him do what we cannot do. He will invisibly grow His strength within us. Like a tree.

Our "effort" is simply to keep the soil of our heart "willing". Are you "willing" to receive spirit-seeds, from Christ's words of compassion, into your heart? Water them with gratitude and your spirit will grow like a tree planted by the rivers of water. He will automatically motivate you to produce fruit. We learn to sink into God, relax and let God love us, then pass it on, this is our work.

John 6:29KJV "Jesus answered and said unto them, This is the work of God, that ye believe on him whom He hath sent."

When we feed on God's Word, it becomes like an invisible "seed planted" within our spirit that will grow with time. Psalm 1:3 KJV. "*And he shall be like a tree planted by the rivers of water, that bringeth forth his fruit in His season; his leaf also shall not wither; and whatsoever he doeth shall prosper.*

Scripture summarizes the simple process of maturing into wine: Psalm 37:3 & 7 KJV – *"Trust in the Lord, and do good … Rest in the Lord, and wait patiently for Him: fret not thyself …"* In other words, we do what we can and leave the results to God.

Haggai 2:9 KJV *"The glory of this latter house shall be greater than of the former, saith the Lord of hosts: and in this place will I give peace, saith the Lord of hosts."*

PERSONAL APPLICATION:

 The Bible says Jesus Christ is the Living Word, the Word made flesh. Therefore, as you focus on Him, and REST IN HIS LOVE, you are maturing in the wine of Christ's Spirit. "Being confident of this very thing, that He which hath begun a good work in you will perform it until the day of Jesus Christ." (Philippians 1:6 KJV). Amen.

Psalm 23 KJV

1 "The Lord is my Shepherd; I shall not want.

2 He maketh me to lie down in green pastures: he leadeth me beside the still waters.

3 He restoreth my soul: he leadeth me in the paths of righteousness for his name's sake.

4 Yea, though I walk through the valley of the shadow of death, I will fear no evil: for thou art with me; thy rod and thy staff they comfort me.

5 Thou preparest a table before me in the presence of mine enemies: thou anointest my head with oil: my cup runneth over.

6 Surely goodness and mercy shall follow me all the days of my life: and I will dwell in the house of the Lord for ever."

EPILOGUE

Isaiah 53:4-6 NIV "Surely he took up our infirmities and carried our sorrows ... the punishment that brought us peace was upon him, and by His wounds we are healed.

We all, like sheep, have gone astray, each *of us has turned to his own way; and the Lord has laid on Him the iniquity of us all."*

ETERNAL JUSTICE HAS BEEN PAID, YOU LORD CHRIST HATH SET US FREE, IN LOVE, TO SERVE THEE. Thank you Lord Jesus !!! Amen & Amen.

John 14:18 & 21 NIV "I will not leave you as orphans; I will come to you ... He who loves Me will be loved by my Father, and I too will love him and show myself to him."

IN MEMORY of my good friend Sharon, who died recently after fighting COVID-19 for two months, I want to give honor to her life, and to the Lord for using her to mentor me in prayer and practicing the Presence of God. Sharon was both a Pastor and a Psychologist. Thus, I loved our deep conversations together and looked forward to more. But I take comfort in the fact that she is now healed in Heaven.

Neither Sharon nor I had any natural children, but God gave us many God-kids. In fact, Sharon and her husband had 80 foster children come through their home. They permanently adopted six. This whole family just kept loving and giving, and God made them fruitful.

Isaiah 54:1-3 NIV "Sing, O barren woman (OR BARREN LIFE), you who never bore a child, burst into song ... because more are the children of the desolate ... Enlarge the place of your tent ... do not hold back; lengthen your cords, strengthen your stakes. For you will spread out to the right and to the left.

In a prayer line one time at church, where Sharon and other pastors were praying for people, I could see through my eyelids that there was a light-being walking across the stage to them. But, when I opened my eyes, it was just people praying. But, in the invisible realm, LIGHT appeared, and I saw it with my eyes closed. It was as if their prayers opened the door for Jesus or one of His angels to supernaturally join us in fellowship. It reminded me of these scriptures:

1 John 1:5 NIV "... GOD IS LIGHT; in Him there is no darkness at all."

Psalm 104:2 KJV "Who coverest thyself with LIGHT as with a garment."

John 8:12 NIV "When Jesus spoke again to the people, he said, 'I AM THE LIGHT OF THE WORLD. WHOEVER FOLLOWS ME WILL NEVER WALK

IN DARKNESS, BUT WILL HAVE THE LIGHT OF LIFE.'"

Because I could feel positive tangible energy flow through Sharon when she prayed, I asked her "what do you visualize, or think about when you are praying for people?" She said that she pictures her heart going deep into Jesus' heart. Then she stays there and lets His Love flow out to the people she lays hands on. Sharon, indeed, found her "hiding place" in God (Psalm 32:7 KJV). May we pause often, and go there too. He is our true home, where we become our true selves in the Presence of God.

HONORING FRIENDS AND FAMILY

Thank you to those who have edified me by sharing their God-moments, too. These stories include timely coincidences of people and provision which came into their lives, just in time, when they needed it most. Some affectionately call these "God-incidences," or "Smiles from God," or "God-winks." Never taking it for granted, I believe Godly coincidences are meant to evoke deep gratitude to God. This deep gratitude is the "wine" of maturing in Christ. Deep gratitude should result from all "Godly" spiritual experiences.

Friends and family have also shared impressive "spirit-awareness" and "spirit-connections." But because supernatural experiences are so personal, they often are not shared publicly. Therefore, here are a few stories, protecting confidentiality by not mentioning names.

Also a scripture of caution to keep us "safe" in the spirit realm: 1 John 4:1-2 NIV *"Dear friends, do not believe every spirit, but test the spirits to see whether they are from God... Every spirit that acknowledges that Jesus Christ has come in the flesh is from God."*

In other words, check your inward witness, then outwardly praise Jesus for coming in the flesh and for Resurrecting from the dead. If the "invisible" spirit cannot praise Christ with you, tell it "in Jesus Name begone" so that you set a boundary between yourself and any harassing spirit. Remember, "Greater is He that is in you, than he that is in the world" (1 John 4:4 KJV). If however, God has led you to minister to a "visible" unbeliever, speak life and love into them in Jesus Name, then let God do His compassionate inner work. Continue in your own heart and mouth praising Jesus, since God "inhabits" the praises of His people (Psalm 22:3 KJV). No fear, God is always near.

We who have surrendered to Christ are connected to Christ and others through His Spirit, like a Divine Internet. Whether in Heaven or still on earth, we are never alone, we are always connected by the Holy Spirit. Prayerfully enjoy these authentic stories, in Jesus Name:

S.L. talks about feeling her mother's loving spirit for about a month after she died. S.L. also felt her cousin's loving spirit come to her in the kitchen a few minutes before the phone rang. It was her cousin calling from 500 miles north. These two experiences of feeling a spiritual connection with her departed mother, then another spiritual connection with her living cousin, convinced her we are all connected by Christ's Divine Internet, we are never alone. S.L. also talks about feeling an invisible loving Presence, as if it were the Lord or an angel, when she faced medical challenges. Also, a dream about ICorinthians 13 came to her when she needed to know what Christ's supernatural Love looked like. That was the first Bible verse that came to her through a dream. God is love, and He will make Himself known to receptive hearts.

E.V. talks about seeing her beloved father briefly after he had died. Early one morning just a quick appearance in the easy chair, a quick smile and he was gone again. But, his visit, his smile created abiding joy within her heart and gave her great peace. E.V. seeks God at a deep level to help her through a lifetime of experiencing a congenital disorder, and He has healed her time and time again. E.V. loves to meditate on scriptures which infuse her with life on a deep level. She is a wonderful example of Psalm 1:3 which speaks of the end effect of meditating on scripture: We become like trees planted by rivers of water. E.V. is someone who both appears and behaves as if she has a river of life flowing through her. Her children and husband are the beneficiaries of her supernatural calm amidst the storms of life. Her continual prayer lifestyle, intrinsic joy and love, positively infect all of us who are privileged to be found among her friends.

C.S. talks about how God delivered her family supernaturally, after World War II, from confinement in East Germany. She also talks about being stalked as a child during those war-torn years where people were emotionally off-balance, and yet God gave her super-natural energy to outrun danger. God also talked to her in His whisper during the day, sometimes warning her, sometimes directing her, as well as in her dreams. Her life since then has been abundant fruitfulness and generosity to many in need. Her friendship with Christ radiates love to her family and all of us.

K.T. talks about her auto accident where she was pinned under her RV for three hours, but not alone. She could feel the angels all around her, and she experienced supernatural peace. Her swift recovery afterwards also amazed her medical doctors and surgeons. God became real to her, and to us as she shared her story. She is a nurse. So, her experience included her scientific mind observing all her physical reactions. But God's calm took her through. Still does daily.

K.D. talks about her experience with a tumor on her thyroid when her daughters were very young. A special scan diagnosed her tumor as a cold nodule, which she was told is usually cancerous. She felt so distressed and unable to sleep, that she took a prayer-walk in the middle of the night to talk to the Lord. She told God that she was ready to go to Him but was concerned about who would raise her young daughters. She poured out her heart to God and surrendered her concerns to Him. A great PEACE came over her, enveloped her, covered her, as she was praying and walking. She knew God was with her. In her next doctor's appointment, they determined that her tumor had surprisingly disappeared. They could not explain it. Science indeed helps us when we need it, but this time it wasn't needed. Since then, K.D. has seen both daughters married and successful in their lives and work. Now she is also enjoying grandchildren. Humbled by it all, she continues to love God, and her love is felt by all those who know her.

A.B. talks about her fall off a cliff. She felt as if she were in slow motion, as if angels were carrying her down. She could have broken her neck and died, but only her heel was injured. It was not her time to go. Years later she helped her husband regain his health after spending two months in the hospital with COVID-19. God has given them both supernatural energy in what's referred to as "finishing season." But, they aren't finished yet, as they are so energetic with God's supernatural help. They love and laugh a lot. Well done friends.

G.G. talks about her spirit floating out of her body at the beginning of a serious surgery, and she went to the ceiling and looked down. She was surprised to see another surgeon in the room. Then, in her post-op appointment she asked her doctor who that extra person was. He was surprised that she saw him but explained that they usually ask for a back-up surgeon to be present in case of an emergency. He of course was impressed by her "unusual awareness" that she had. Her doctors told her she might not have children in the future. But, despite naysayers, she later had three children. She also became an accomplished Psychologist, MFT, where she administers EMDR, which helps military recover from PTSD as well as all of us who have had any trauma in life. In her therapy to others, one of her favorite sayings is the reminder to TURN TO GOD, AND NOT AWAY at every challenge in life. Her grandchildren, friends, and family all love her hugs, as if that God-energy, love-energy from the invisible realm makes Himself known, and that we are not alone.

The Lord is our Shepherd, we shall not want ...

The Lord IS our Shepherd, we shall not want...

Rest in His Love, and pass it on.

Made in the USA
Las Vegas, NV
13 September 2021

30210089R00031